CONTENTS

GW00578050

Extra Resources

We have provided a number of extra resources to accompany this *'Song and Story'* book/CD. **Visit our website at www.outoftheark.co.uk/resources to download**:

- Story/script in a child-friendly font so children can read as they listen to the narrated story *(CD track 1)*
- Mini-books with simplified story (for easy reading) and space to illustrate the story
- Lyric sheets

Percussion Notes

Percussion parts are included for all the songs *(see music score)* and we have also suggested areas in the script where percussion can be used for sound effects. Encouraging the children to play along with the songs will enrich their musical experience, helping with co-ordination and teamwork. Have fun including as much as you like and experiment with making other 'instruments' from everyday objects you might find at home or in the classroom.

Cast List

Speaking parts:

Narrator Suitable for a teacher or easily divided into shorter sections for a number of different children.

Mother Someone with a good 'wagging finger and hands on hips' stance! Just a couple of lines to remember.

Jack A few short, easy lines to say, but good acting skills would be handy.

Butcher The giver of the beans! Just one short line to say.

Wife The giant's wife, with two short lines. A kind, motherly type would be ideal.

Giant A good strong speaking voice is essential for this role. Someone with an aptitude for 'Fee, fi, fo, fumming'!

Harp A child dressed in gold/yellow. A large piece of cardboard could be cut to the shape of the child's body (when bent) with the strings of the harp painted on. They arch around the card as they pretend to play. One very small line to learn.

Ideas for non-speaking parts:

There are relatively few speaking parts in this musical, however there are lots of opportunities to involve more children throughout the play. The main body of your performers can stand in the 'choir', with some playing percussion (see page 2). You could allocate others the following roles and to set the scene:

The cow A pantomime cow approach would be perfect.

Passers-by A few children needed for Jack to pass/call to on his way to market.

The hen Use your imagination with this one – but feathers and clucking spring to mind!

The beanstalk

A few children, dressed in green with the odd leaf attached, could entwine themselves together, crouching low to begin with. As the beanstalk grows, they slowly stand, then gradually push up a pre-made stalk to reach even higher.

Script and Song Lyrics

NARRATOR   Once upon a time there was a widow who lived in a little cottage with her only son, Jack. They were very poor and as time passed they became poorer and poorer, until finally, all they had left was one cow.

Jack's mother decided there was only one thing to do. She called Jack to her.

MOTHER   You must take the cow to the market.

NARRATOR   Jack's mother asked him to get a good price for the cow. So he set off down the road to the market.

Jack passed some people on the way. He shouted out to them…

JACK   Cow for sale, cow for sale!

Song 1.   COW FOR SALE   CD track 2/7

1 One fine cow, one fine cow.
   Who would like to buy a cow?
   With very nice hooves and a long brown tail,
   Cow for sale!

2 One fine cow, one fine cow.
   Who would like to buy a cow?
   She's just like new with a very fine 'moo',
   Cow for sale!

3 One fine cow, one fine cow.
   Who would like to buy a cow?
   With pure white milk and ears like silk,
   Cow for sale!

4 Repeat verse 1

NARRATOR   Then Jack met a butcher. The butcher offered to buy the cow.

BUTCHER   I will give you these magic beans for your cow.

JACK   Magic beans! Yes please!

NARRATOR   So the butcher took the cow and Jack took the beans home to show his mother. But his mother was very angry and she threw the beans out of the window.

MOTHER   What good are these beans to us? Go straight to bed Jack!

NARRATOR   That night the beans sprouted and began to grow.[1] In the morning, when Jack looked out of his window, he saw an amazing beanstalk that stretched right up into the sky. Jack was very excited. He went out to the beanstalk and began to climb.

Up, up, up he went, higher and higher.

Song 2.   CLIMBING UP THE BEANSTALK   CD track 3/8

1 Off Jack went, climbing up the beanstalk,
Off Jack went, climbing high.
Up, up, up, up, up,
Into the sky, sky, sky,
Into the sky.

2 Off Jack went, through the green leaves,
Far away from the ground.
Up, up, up, up, up,
Into the clouds, clouds, clouds,
Into the clouds.

3 Repeat verse 1

NARRATOR   At the top of the beanstalk was a wonderful, strange land and an enormous castle. Jack walked up to the great wooden door.

---

1 **Added percussion:** Use a slide whistle gradually getting higher, or rising notes on a glockenspiel to represent the growing beanstalk.

A woman opened the door. She was the wife of the big, bad giant who lived in the castle.

WIFE   Go away or my husband, the giant, will eat you up!

JACK   But I'm hungry and tired.

NARRATOR   The wife felt sorry for Jack so she took him into the kitchen and gave him something to eat.

Suddenly, there were three very loud knocks on the door. Jack could hear big heavy feet getting closer and closer.[2] The giant had come home.

GIANT   FEE, FI, FO, FUM!

Song 3.   FEE, FI, FO, FUM   CD track 4/9

1 Fee, fi, fo, fum,
   I smell the blood of an Englishman.
   Be he alive or be he dead,
   I'll grind his bones to make my bread.
   Fee, fi, fee, fo, fum.

2 Fee, fi, fo, fum,
   I am a giant, I weigh a ton.
   Eating you would be lots of fun,
   So I think you had better run.
   Fee, fi, fee, fo, fum.

3 Repeat verse 1

© 2009 Out of the Ark Ltd, Surrey KT12 4RQ
CCLI Song No. 5304301

WIFE   Go and hide in that cupboard, away from the giant.

GIANT   FEE, FI, FO, FUM!

---

2   **Added percussion:** Use claves or a woodblock for the knocks and a low drum sound for the heavy footsteps.

NARRATOR	The giant sat at the table. His wife gave him an enormous dinner and told him that he must be imagining things. The giant ate his dinner, then shouted to his wife…
GIANT	Bring me my hen!
NARRATOR	His wife brought him the hen, then the giant shouted…
GIANT	LAY ME AN EGG!
NARRATOR	The hen laid a beautiful golden egg.
GIANT	LAY ME ANOTHER EGG!
NARRATOR	The hen laid several golden eggs. Then the giant roared,
GIANT	BRING ME MY HARP!
NARRATOR	The giant's wife brought him a wonderful, golden harp, put it on the table, then went off to bed. The giant shouted at the harp…
GIANT	PLAY ME A TUNE!
NARRATOR	The harp played the most beautiful, haunting music.

Song 4.   THE GIANT'S HARP　　　　CD track 5/10
(Instrumental with simple percussion)

NARRATOR	The giant became sleepier and sleepier until finally his head rested on the table and he began to snore. Jack ran out of the cupboard and grabbed the hen and the harp, but the harp cried out…
HARP	Help master, help master!
NARRATOR	The giant woke up.
GIANT	FEE, FI, FO, FUM!
NARRATOR	Jack ran out of the castle as fast as his legs could carry him. He ran and ran but the giant was close behind. Jack began to

climb down the beanstalk. Down, down, down as fast as he could.[3] He called to his mother…

JACK   Mother, get an axe!

NARRATOR   His mother brought the axe and Jack chopped the beanstalk right in two. The giant came toppling down. He landed with a mighty crash and that was the end of him.[4]

Song 5.   DOWN CAME THAT MIGHTY BEANSTALK

CD track 6/11

1 Chop, chop went the axe,
   Chop, chop went the axe,
   And down came that mighty beanstalk.

2 Creak, creak went the stalk,
   Creak, creak went the stalk,
   And down came that mighty beanstalk.

3 'Oh, no!' the giant said,
   'Oh, no!' the giant said,
   And down came that mighty beanstalk.

4 That's how the story ends,
   That's how the story ends,
   They never saw that giant again,
   They never saw that giant again.

NARRATOR   With the golden eggs and the harp, Jack and his mother never had to worry about being poor again and they lived happily ever after.

If time allows, a repeat of 'Down Came That Mighty Beanstalk' would work well to end the play.

---

3 **Added percussion:** Use the slide whistle or glockenspiel descending as Jack climbs down.
4 **Added percussion:** Crash two cymbals together as the giant falls.

Cow For Sale

Words and Music by
Niki Davies

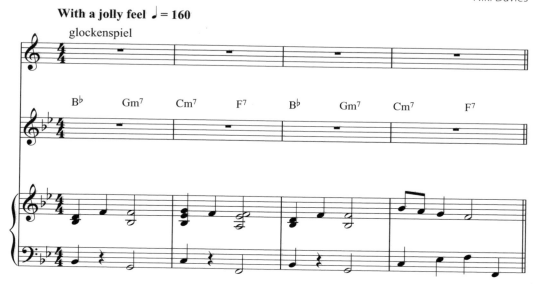

One fine cow, one fine cow. Who would like to

buy a cow? { 1. With ve - ry nice hooves and a long brown tail,
{ 3. With pure white milk and ears like silk,

cow for sale!
cow for sale!

One fine cow, one fine cow. Who would like to
One fine cow, one fine cow. Who would like to

buy a cow? 2. She's just like new with a ve-ry fine 'moo',
buy a cow? 4. With ve-ry nice hooves and a long brown tail,

cow for sale!
cow for

sale!

Climbing Up The Beanstalk

Words and Music by
Niki Davies

Fee, Fi, Fo, Fum

Words and Music by
Niki Davies

grind his bones to   make my bread.   Fee,   fi,   fee,   fo,
I think you had   bet - ter   run.   Fee,   fi,   fee,   fo,

1. 2.

fum.
fum.

3.

fum.

The Giant's Harp

Music by Niki Davies

CCLI Song No. 5304325

Down Came That Mighty Beanstalk

Words and Music by
Niki Davies

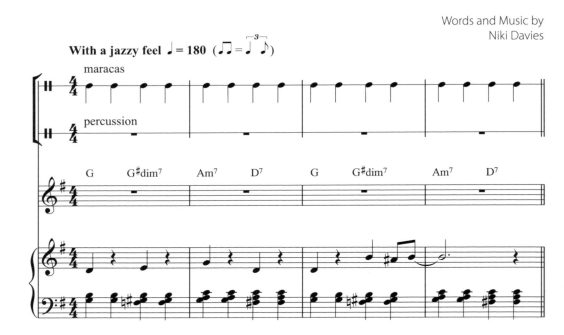

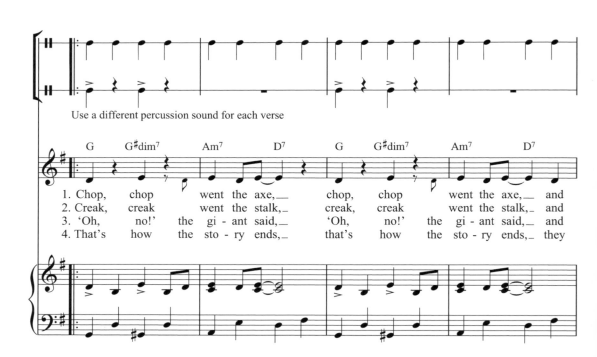

1. Chop, chop went the axe,— chop, chop went the axe,— and
2. Creak, creak went the stalk,— creak, creak went the stalk,— and
3. 'Oh, no!' the gi - ant said,— 'Oh, no!' the gi - ant said,— and
4. That's how the sto - ry ends,— that's how the sto - ry ends,— they

Use a different percussion sound for each verse

Copyright & Licensing

VERY IMPORTANT

You are free to use the material in our musicals for all teaching purposes. However the performance of musicals or songs to an audience and the reproduction of scripts, lyrics and music scores are subject to licensing requirements by law. A free licence for certain performances is available on the CD provided with this songbook – see below for details.

Helpful information about licensing can also be found on the following website:

'A Guide to Licensing Copyright in Schools' www.licensing-copyright.org

And remember, we're happy to help. For advice contact our customer services team:

UK: 01932 232 250   International: +44 1932 232 250   copyright@outoftheark.com

---

(1) Performance of Musicals

The performance of a work involving drama, movement, narrative or dialogue such as a musical requires a specific licence from the publisher. **Your PRS licence does not cover musicals.**

If your school is performing *Jack and the Beanstalk* by Niki Davies as a musical on school premises, to an audience of staff, pupils and their families, then to simplify the process we have already issued an inclusive licence that grants permission to stage a performance.

If you are performing *Jack and the Beanstalk* for any other type of audience please contact Out of the Ark Music directly to apply for a performance licence.

(2) Licensing of Audio and Video Recordings

To make an audio or video recording please contact Out of the Ark Music directly.

(3) Other use of the published material

If you are not staging a musical but still intend to use material from the publication then different licences are required:

(a) Reproduction of Song Lyrics or Musical Scores
The following licences from Christian Copyright Licensing Ltd (www.ccli.com) permit photocopying or reproduction of song lyrics and music scores, for example to create song-sheets, overhead transparencies or to use any electronic display medium.

For UK schools: 'Collective Worship Copyright Licence' and 'Music Reproduction Licence.'
For churches: 'Church Copyright and Music Reproduction Licence.'

Please ensure that you log the songs that are used on your copy report. (Organisations that do not hold one of the above licences should contact Out of the Ark Music directly for permission.)

(b) Performance of Songs
If you are not staging a musical but are performing any of our songs for the public on school premises (i.e. for anybody other than staff and pupils) then royalty payments become due. Most schools have an arrangement with the Performing Rights Society (PRS) through their local authority. Organisations that do not have such an arrangement should contact Out of the Ark Music directly.